이그잼보카 고등
1000

KB076684

목차

Day 1

TEST

번호	영어	한글
1	melancholy	
2	obscure	
3	more often than not	
4	bring A to a stop	
5	capacity	
6	sarcastic	
7	set out	
8	adjust A around B	
9	watchful	
10	at no cost	
11	approximate	
12	drawback	
13	refuse	
14	predominant	
15	intervene	
16	for fear of	
17	substitute	
18	unearth	
19	standpoint	
20	be absorbed in	

TEST

번호	유의어	반의어	영어	글자수
21	aroma, fragrance, smell	stench, odor	S	5
22	plenty, wealth, profusion	Scarcity, shortage, dearth	A	8
23	fit, convulsion, attack	release, letting go, relinquishment	S	7
24	precision, correctness, exactness	inaccuracy, imprecision, error	A	8
25	unaffected, unharmed, undamaged	better, improved, enhanced	N	12 (p.)
26	standing, upright, on foot	off one's feet, sitting, lying down	O	11 (p.)
27	melt, liquefy, disintegrate	Solidify, congeal, coagulate	D	8
28	hurry, rush, speed	leisure, slowness	H	5
29	comment, observation, statement	ignore, disregard	R	6
30	divert, avert, turn aside	attract, draw, allure	D	7
31	owe, burdened with debt, in debt	Clear, settle, pay off	I	6
32	compliment, praise, sweet-talk	insult, criticize	F	7
33	be vulnerable to N, be susceptible to N, be liable to N	be immune to N, be unaffected by N, be exempt from N	B	12 (p.)
34	thwart, hinder, impede	assist, aid	F	9
35	own, have, hold	lack, be without	P	7
36	harmful to N, detrimental to N, injurious to N	beneficial to N, advantageous to N, helpful to N	D	11 (p.)
37	magnetic force, attraction, magnetization	Non-magnetic, non-attractive, non-repulsive	M	9
38	fantastic, incredible, marvelous	Unimpressive, ordinary, unexceptional	F	8
39	distribute, assign, allot	withhold, retain, keep	A	8
40	luxurious, lavish, opulent	plain, simple, modest	S	9

Day 2

번호	영어	한글
41	impure	
42	keen	
43	back out	
44	cease to do	
45	utmost	
46	preside	
47	pity	
48	barren	
49	determine	
50	vine	
51	endure	
52	illuminate	
53	arise	
54	neural	
55	divert	
56	react to N	
57	prominent	
58	compost	
59	outlandish	
60	given that	

* 유의어와 반의어에 '0'이 있는 문제는 해당 어휘가 없는 경우이니 그냥 패스하시면 됩니다. 글자수의 (p.)는 '숙어' 표시입니다.

번호	유의어	반의어	영어	글자수
61	force, oblige, require	discourage, dissuade, deter	C	6
62	partnership, coalition, union	Enmity, rivalry, opposition	A	8
63	absolute, complete, total	ambiguous, unclear, uncertain	O	8
64	supporter, sponsor, benefactor	Critic, opponent, adversary	P	6
65	excess, extra, surplusage	Deficiency, shortage, insufficiency	S	7
66	respect, admire, regard highly	disrespect, disdain, contempt	E	6
67	persist, endure, continue	Quit, give up, surrender	P	9
68	reside, occupy, dwell	vacate, abandon, desert	I	7
69	emphasize, highlight, stress	de-emphasize, downplay, minimize	A	10
70	impartial, unbiased, neutral	biased, partial, prejudiced	D	13
71	prohibition, restriction, ban	Acceptable, permissible, allowed	T	5
72	important, meaningful, substantial	Insignificant, unimportant, trivial	S	11
73	for a fee of, for a price of, at a cost of	free of charge, without charge, at no cost	A	11 (p.)
74	understand, grasp, comprehend	be confused about, be uncertain about, be unclear about	H	13 (p.)
75	suggest, insinuate, indicate	deny, contradict	I	5
76	likelihood is, it's probable that, it's likely that	chances aren't, it's improbable that	C	10 (p.)
77	hairless, barren, bald-headed	hairy, furry, well-covered	B	4
78	consist of, include, encompass	Exclude, omit, leave out	C	8
79	follow, chase, seek	retreat, abandon, surrender	P	6
80	entice, lure, seduce	deter, dissuade, discourage	T	5

Day 3

번호	영어	한글
81	restrict	
82	in an effort to do	
83	eccentric	
84	merge into	
85	grief	
86	privilege	
87	cultivate	
88	marvel	
89	belong to N	
90	fit in with	
91	retrospect	
92	bruise	
93	extinguish	
94	tribe	
95	carry on	
96	apparent	
97	shiver	
98	enter into	
99	frank	
100	condemn	

* 유의어와 반의어에 '0'이 있는 문제는 해당 어휘가 없는 경우이니 그냥 패스하시면 됩니다. 글자수의 (p.)는 '숙어' 표시입니다.

번호	유의어	반의어	영어	글자수
101	shared, common, reciprocal	individual, separate	M	6
102	restrain, suppress, hinder	encourage, stimulate	I	7
103	influence, affect, make a difference to	have no effect on, be inconsequential to, be insignificant to	H	14 (p.)
104	inclined, disposed, likely	upright, vertical, standing	P	5
105	have a good relationship with, get on with, be compatible with	clash with, disagree with, conflict with	G	12 (p.)
106	eject, remove, oust	Admit, accept, welcome	E	5
107	tall grass, marsh plant, cane	Hard, firm, rigid	R	4
108	process, assimilate, metabolize	regurgitate, vomit	D	6
109	framework, structure, charter	Destruction, disintegration, breakdown	C	12
110	obstructing, blocking, hindering	out of the way, clear, unobstructed	I	8 (p.)
111	redden, blush, glow	drain, deplete, empty	F	5
112	skilled, competent, capable	inexperienced, unskilled, inept	P	10
113	mathematics, mathematical study, spatial relationships	Non-geometry, non-mathematics, non-mathematical	G	8
114	clean, clear, broom	scatter, disperse	D	5
115	detailed, intricate, complex	simplify, condense	E	9
116	story, tale, narrative	Fact, reality, truth	A	8
117	repair, renew, revive	Ruin, damage, destroy	R	7
118	crush, squash, pulp	uncrush, separate, disconnect	M	4
119	sample, example, representative	Entirety, whole, complete entity	S	8
120	brutal, ruthless, inhumane	kind, compassionate	C	5

Day 4

번호	영어	한글
121	as it were	
122	coordinate	
123	perplex	
124	drain	
125	comet	
126	alternative	
127	ruin	
128	appropriate	
129	beware	
130	by heart	
131	limp	
132	get into shape	
133	suffix	
134	distort	
135	devastate	
136	wholesome	
137	statement	
138	legitimate	
139	confess	
140	come in handy	

ˋ 유의어와 반의어에 '0'이 있는 문제는 해당 어휘가 없는 경우이니 그냥 패스하시면 됩니다. 글자수의 (p.)는 '숙어' 표시입니다.

번호	유의어	반의어	영어	글자수
141	wire, connect, establish a connection	Wireless, cordless, untethered	H	8
142	carnivore, hunter, killer	Prey, victim, target	P	8
143	surpass, outperform, excel	Underperform, fall short, do worse	O	5
144	delicate, breakable, frail	sturdy, robust	F	7
145	be connected to, be affixed to	detach from, separate from	B	12 (p.)
146	multiple, several, various	singular, singular form, singular number	P	6
147	dense, compressed, closely packed	Large, spacious, roomy	C	7
148	reverse, flip, turn upside down	Retain, keep, maintain	I	6
149	be aware of, be mindful of	be unaware of, oblivious to	B	13 (p.)
150	extend, lengthen, protract	shorten, abbreviate	P	7
151	oust, topple, depose	Uphold, preserve, maintain	O	9
152	noteworthy, remarkable, prominent	Insignificant, unimportant, ordinary	N	7
153	bow and arrow, marksmanship, shooting	Non-archery, absence of bow and arrow use	A	7
154	consume, devour, subsist on	starve, abstain from, refrain from	F	6 (p.)
155	boomerang, rebound, misfire	Succeed, go well, work out	B	8
156	end, conclude, finish	initiate, begin	T	9
157	worship, love, venerate	despise, detest	A	5
158	debris, ruins, wreckage remains	Intact, undamaged, unharmed	W	8
159	legislature, congress, governing body	Non-parliament, non-legislative body, non-congress	P	10
160	upright, standing, vertical	dismantle, disassemble, take apart	E	5

Day 5

번호	영어	한글
161	debate	
162	column	
163	imperial	
164	vessel	
165	desolate	
166	have a breakdown	
167	come out	
168	listless	
169	hand in	
170	back down	
171	sacrifice	
172	lessen	
173	half off	
174	startle	
175	appeal to N	
176	nerve	
177	console	
178	verbal	
179	cumulative	
180	humid	

* 유의어와 반의어에 '0'이 있는 문제는 해당 어휘가 없는 경우이니 그냥 패스하시면 됩니다. 글자수의 (p.)는 '숙어' 표시입니다.

번호	유의어	반의어	영어	글자수
181	ponder, contemplate, consider	conceal, hide	R	7
182	committee, assembly, board	individual, person	C	7
183	differentiate, segregate, distinguish	integrate, include	D	12
184	get in trouble, get into difficulties, encounter problems	stay out of trouble, avoid trouble, steer clear of trouble	G	14 (p.)
185	hollow, pit, cavity	Hill, mound, elevation	C	6
186	according to one, from one's perspective, in one's view	objectively, factually, empirically	I	14 (p.)
187	illogical, unreasonable, nonsensical	Rational, logical, reasonable	I	10
188	have the ability to, be able to	be incapable of, unable to	B	11 (p.)
189	24/7, continuously	intermittently, occasionally	A	14 (p.)
190	reverse, cancel, overturn	do, perform	U	4
191	illegal, unlawful, prohibited	legal, lawful, permitted	A	14 (p.)
192	in the next year, in the forthcoming year, in the upcoming year	in the past year, in the previous year, in the preceding year	I	15 (p.)
193	air, environment, ambiance	Vacuum, emptiness, void	A	10
194	wait, pause, hang on	let go, release, relinquish	H	6 (p.)
195	in discussion with, in collaboration with, in coordination with	independently of, unilaterally, without consulting	I	18 (p.)
196	admit, recognize, confess	deny, refuse	A	11
197	appear, surface, come forth	disappear, vanish	E	6
198	inclined to, disposed to, feeling like	uninterested in, disinclined to, unwilling to	I	12 (p.)
199	damage, weaken, diminish	enhance, improve, strengthen	I	6
200	essential, crucial, important	nonessential, insignificant, trivial	V	5

* 유의어와 반의어에 '0'이 있는 문제는 해당 어휘가 없는 경우이니 그냥 패스하시면 됩니다. 글자수의 (p.)는 '숙어' 표시입니다.

Day 6

번호	영어	한글
201	enclosure	
202	free from	
203	sneeze	
204	sob	
205	revenue	
206	nod	
207	get past	
208	injure	
209	pathetic	
210	swift	
211	hospitality	
212	can afford to do	
213	pessimist	
214	breed	
215	monarchy	
216	stitch	
217	insist	
218	in a series	
219	banquet	
220	contradict	

ˋ 유의어와 반의어에 '0'이 있는 문제는 해당 어휘가 없는 경우이니 그냥 패스하시면 됩니다. 글자수의 (p.)는 '숙어' 표시입니다.

번호	유의어	반의어	영어	글자수
221	absorb, comprehend, understand	ignore, overlook, neglect	T	6 (p.)
222	banish, deport, expel	inclusion, acceptance	E	5
223	need only do, merely need to do, simply have to do	be unable to do, be prohibited from doing, be prevented from doing	H	12 (p.)
224	exhaustion, weariness, tiredness	energy, vigor	F	7
225	legacy, inheritance, tradition	Loss, abandonment, abandonment	H	8
226	remove A, clear A, eliminate A	bring A forward, facilitate A, encourage A	G	15 (p.)
227	independently, by oneself, solo	with others, together, collectively	O	10 (p.)
228	eventually, ultimately	in the short term, immediately	I	12 (p.)
229	UV, invisible radiation, ultraviolet light	infrared, visible, visible light	U	11
230	drinkable, suitable for drinking, safe to consume	Non-potable, undrinkable, contaminated	P	7
231	splendid, grand, impressive	Ordinary, unimpressive, mediocre	M	11
232	intentional, calculated, planned	accidental, unintentional, inadvertent	D	10
233	overspend, live beyond one's means, be extravagant	live within one's means, budget, economize	L	21 (p.)
234	dry out, remove moisture, desiccate	Hydrate, moisten, soak	D	9
235	navigator, guide, director	disorient, confuse, mislead	C	7
236	immobile, fixed, motionless	moving, mobile	S	10
237	most, the greater part of, the larger portion of	a minority of, less than half of, a small portion of	A	11 (p.)
238	contents page, index, list of contents	body of text, main text, content	T	15 (p.)
239	involve, necessitate, require	exclude, omit, disregard	E	6
240	accurate, exact, meticulous	Inexact, imprecise, approximate	P	7

Day 7

번호	영어	한글
241	paddle	
242	shrink	
243	halt	
244	smear	
245	blush	
246	reside	
247	thermal	
248	avail oneself of	
249	take A for granted	
250	solemn	
251	aesthetic	
252	call after	
253	be frightened of	
254	popularity	
255	in the face of	
256	accomplish	
257	charity	
258	liable	
259	yield	
260	provision	

TEST

* 유의어와 반의어에 '0'이 있는 문제는 해당 어휘가 없는 경우이니 그냥 패스하시면 됩니다. 글자수의 (p.)는 '숙어' 표시입니다.

번호	유의어	반의어	영어	글자수
261	legally, according to the law, pursuant to law	illegally, unlawfully, criminally	B	5 (p.)
262	opt for, choose, select	avoid, shun, reject	G	5 (p.)
263	inference, conclusion, reasoning	Induction, addition, inclusion	D	9
264	close, personal, familiar	Distant, remote, detached	I	8
265	cut, clip, prune	expand, enlarge, lengthen	T	4
266	converse with, talk to, engage in a discussion with	avoid a discussion with, evade a conversation with	H	19 (p.)
267	standard, guideline, parameter	Irrelevant factor, non-factor, irrelevant aspect	C	9
268	clumsy, ungraceful, ungainly	graceful, coordinated, adept	A	7
269	mental, intellectual, psychological	noncognitive, nonmental	C	9
270	indifferent to N, aloof to N, unresponsive to N	warm to N, affectionate towards N, loving towards N	C	7 (p.)
271	confirm, assert, declare	deny, negate, contradict	A	6
272	persistent, long-term, constant	acute, sudden	C	7
273	severe, rigorous, stern	gentle, mild, soft	H	5
274	strip A of B, rob A of B, deny A access to B	provide A with B, grant A access to B, endow A with B	D	11 (p.)
275	depict, represent, illustrate	Misrepresent, distort, falsify	P	7
276	back, posterior, behind	Front, anterior, fore	R	4
277	universal, all-encompassing, comprehensive	Non-Catholic, non-denominational, non-religious	C	8
278	apart from, aside from	including, encompassing	E	9 (p.)
279	speed, rate, swiftness	Standstill, immobility, inertia	V	8
280	capable of, competent to do, eligible to do	unqualified to do, ineligible to do, incompetent to do	Q	13 (p.)

Day 8

번호	영어	한글
281	act against one's will	
282	draw on	
283	call off	
284	conscience	
285	ferry	
286	abandon	
287	rub	
288	integrate A with B	
289	medieval	
290	insulate	
291	definite	
292	fury	
293	overlook	
294	degenerate	
295	elementary	
296	sneak	
297	irritate	
298	icing	
299	hostage	
300	reluctant	

* 유의어와 반의어에 'O'이 있는 문제는 해당 어휘가 없는 경우이니 그냥 패스하시면 됩니다. 글자수의 (p.)는 '숙어' 표시입니다.

번호	유의어	반의어	영어	글자수
301	discard, cast off, get rid of	Accumulate, gather, collect	S	4
302	empty, clear, vacate	Inhabit, occupy, reside	E	8
303	essential, basic, primary	secondary, nonessential, peripheral	F	11
304	enjoy, appreciate, have a liking for	dislike, have an aversion to, be repelled by	H	13 (p.)
305	artificial, man-made, fabricated	Natural, organic, non-man-made	S	9
306	disadvantage, drawback, fault	Merit, advantage, benefit	D	7
307	assault, attack, incursion	defend, protect, guard	R	4
308	conceptual, theoretical, non-concrete	Concrete, specific, tangible	A	8
309	possibility, capability, potentiality	Non-potential, incapable, incapable of development	P	9
310	remain intact, stay united, stick together	fall apart, disintegrate, collapse	H	12 (p.)
311	water source, storage, tank	Drainage, outflow, depletion	R	9
312	unethical, dishonest, depraved	honest, ethical	C	7
313	pass, adopt, establish	Repeal, abolish, revoke	E	5
314	spot, blemish, discolor	clean, purify	S	5
315	disease, contagion, illness	health, wellness	I	9
316	inexpensively, affordably	at a high price, expensive	A	11 (p.)
317	susceptible to N, at risk of N, prone to N	immune to N, resistant to N, protected from N	V	13 (p.)
318	attribute A to B, credit B with A, ascribe A to B	be indebted to B, be obligated to B, be beholden to B	O	7 (p.)
319	for variety, as a variation, for something different	consistently, habitually, regularly	F	10 (p.)
320	equal, counterpart, colleague	Superior, higher, more advanced	P	4

Day 9

번호	영어	한글
321	at a 형 price	
322	be terrified of	
323	cup of tea	
324	intuition	
325	jump to a conclusion	
326	mobilize	
327	stun	
328	notate	
329	odor	
330	mortgage	
331	vicious	
332	draw A out	
333	conserve	
334	sting	
335	mediate	
336	pendulum	
337	doom	
338	recollect	
339	swallow	
340	adhere	

TEST

번호	유의어	반의어	영어	글자수
341	judgment, decision, ruling	acquittal, exoneration, vindication	V	7
342	celebrate, be happy, delight	mourn, grieve, lament	R	7
343	be accountable for, be responsible for	question, challenge	A	9 (p.)
344	moral principles, morals, values	Unethical behavior, immorality, wrongdoing	E	6
345	decline, diminish, decrease	rise, ascend, increase	F	8 (p.)
346	worry-free, lighthearted, relaxed	worried, anxious, concerned	C	8
347	contingent on, subject to	regardless of, irrespective of	D	11 (p.)
348	endow A with B, imbue A with B, confer B upon A	divest A of B, strip A of B, dispossess A of B	I	12 (p.)
349	amount, quantity, portion	overdose, excessive, surplus	D	4
350	attribute A to B, hold B responsible for A	absolve A from B, exonerate A for	B	9 (p.)
351	meet, confront, face	avoid, evade	E	9
352	admonish, rebuke, scold	praise, commend, applaud	R	7
353	dictator, autocrat, oppressor	Benevolent ruler, just leader, fair monarch	T	6
354	firstly, on the one side, from one perspective	on the other hand, conversely, contrarily	O	9 (p.)
355	energetic, lively, vigorous	Static, motionless, unchanging	D	7
356	fame, reputation, celebrity	obscurity, anonymity, unknown status	R	6
357	seat of power, royal chair, sovereignty	Common seat, ordinary chair, everyday bench	T	6
358	copy, replicate, reproduce	Original, prototype, one-of-a-kind	D	9
359	remain, loiter, stay	rush, hurry	L	6
360	come together, fit together, make sense	fall apart, disintegrate, collapse	F	13 (p.)

Day 10

번호	영어	한글
361	misery	
362	insure	
363	opposite to N	
364	defeat	
365	sustain	
366	consist in	
367	scorn	
368	surpass	
369	edible	
370	compress	
371	set an example of	
372	transmit	
373	polish	
374	optical	
375	encyclopedia	
376	costly	
377	fate	
378	relieve	
379	sheer	
380	do one's part in	

ˋ 유의어와 반의어에 '0'이 있는 문제는 해당 어휘가 없는 경우이니 그냥 패스하시면 됩니다. 글자수의 (p.)는 '숙어' 표시입니다.

번호	유의어	반의어	영어	글자수
381	teenager, youth, young adult	Adult, mature, grown-up	A	10
382	set free, liberate, unleash	hold, retain	R	7
383	overturn, turn around, flip	Forward, progress, advancement	R	7
384	give, award, bestow	Deny, refuse, reject	G	5
385	examine, scrutinize, check	ignore, neglect, overlook	I	7
386	holy, divine, consecrated	Profane, secular, unholy	S	6
387	outdated, outmoded, antiquated	current, modern	O	8
388	in advance of, before, prior to	behind, after, following	A	7 (p.)
389	illumination, insight, awareness	Ignorance, unawareness, lack of knowledge	E	13
390	management, governance, leadership	Rebellion, insurgency, revolt	A	14
391	a group of, a collection of, a cluster of	an individual, a single entity, a lone item	A	8 (p.)
392	bay, inlet, cove	Connection, linkage, unity	G	4
393	flaw, imperfection, fault	asset, advantage	D	6
394	compulsory, required, obligatory	Optional, voluntary, discretionary	M	9
395	promotion, advertising, exposure	Privacy, obscurity, anonymity	P	9
396	motivate, encourage, influence	Discourage, demotivate, dishearten	I	7
397	downgrade, reduce, lower	promote, advance, elevate	D	6
398	in the event of, if, should	regardless of, despite, in spite of	I	8 (p.)
399	compare, equate, analogize	Differentiate, distinguish, contrast	L	5
400	eventually, ultimately, wind up	start, begin, initiate	E	5 (p.)

Day 11

번호	영어	한글
401	discipline	
402	at the least	
403	intent on	
404	desperate	
405	keep up to date	
406	outcast	
407	sow	
408	furnish	
409	designate	
410	competent	
411	suit	
412	deplete	
413	permit	
414	overtake	
415	gratitude	
416	at the height of	
417	stall	
418	comply	
419	underpin	
420	enrich	

* 유의어와 반의어에 'O'이 있는 문제는 해당 어휘가 없는 경우이니 그냥 패스하시면 됩니다. 글자수의 (p.)는 '숙어' 표시입니다.

번호	유의어	반의어	영어	글자수
421	oppose, withstand, defy	yield, surrender	R	6
422	impulsive, unplanned, natural	planned, deliberate, intentional	S	11
423	thief, intruder, robber	homeowner, resident	B	7
424	financial, fiscal, economic	Non-monetary, non-financial, non-cash	M	8
425	inform, tell	keep the news from, conceal the news from	B	14 (p.)
426	chaos, confusion, disarray	order, organization, arrangement	D	8
427	tear, rip, slice	assemble, unite, join	S	5
428	unclear, indefinite, ambiguous	clear, distinct, precise	V	5
429	occurrence, event, happening	Normality, regular occurrence, common event	P	10
430	charge, indict, allege	exonerate, vindicate, absolve	A	6
431	empathetic, compassionate, understanding	apathetic, indifferent	E	8
432	dedicate, commit, consecrate	neglect, ignore	D	6
433	decrease, lessen, diminish	increase, enlarge, expand	R	6
434	ancient, prehistoric, primitive	advanced, modern	P	9
435	order, command, proclamation	repeal, annul	D	6
436	be targeted at, be directed towards	be deterred from, be discouraged from	B	9 (p.)
437	infancy, beginnings, starting point	Tomb, grave, resting place	C	6
438	cherished, adored, dear	despised, detested, loathed	B	7
439	lethal, fatal, mortal	harmless, nonlethal	D	6
440	balance, harmony, proportion	Asymmetry, imbalance, irregularity	S	8

Day 12

번호	영어	한글
441	invaluable	
442	have difficulty in -ing	
443	exterminate	
444	compatible	
445	rag	
446	clone	
447	conceive	
448	in a word	
449	have no choice but to do	
450	vertical	
451	eternal	
452	act upon	
453	shrug	
454	flourish	
455	absorb	
456	abrupt	
457	attribute	
458	concise	
459	diplomacy	
460	mutation	

* 유의어와 반의어에 '0'이 있는 문제는 해당 어휘가 없는 경우이니 그냥 패스하시면 됩니다. 글자수의 (p.)는 '숙어' 표시입니다.

번호	유의어	반의어	영어	글자수
461	talent, capability, skill	Inaptitude, incompetence, lack of skill	A	8
462	consulate, diplomatic mission, foreign office	Host country, local authorities, consulate	E	7
463	mark, impression, stamp	Erase, delete, remove	I	7
464	upset, disappoint, offend	satisfy, please	D	9
465	agreed, united, in accord	divided, split	U	9
466	candid, frank, forthright	reserved, quiet, reticent	O	9
467	grasp, seize, capture	release, let go of, relinquish	C	11 (p.)
468	viewpoint, standpoint, outlook	Myopia, narrow view, limited outlook	P	11
469	frenzied, panicked, wild	Calm, composed, collected	F	7
470	productive, fruitful, rich	barren, infertile, unproductive	F	7
471	to the extent that, as far as, inasmuch as	to the extent that, to the degree that, only if	I	9 (p.)
472	ceremony, tradition, custom	Non-ritual, absence of ceremony, lack of tradition	R	6
473	entice, attract, tempt	repel, deter	L	4
474	reassess, reconfirm, reexamine	invalidate, disapprove, reject, revoke	R	10
475	separate, disconnect, disengage	attach, connect, affix	D	6
476	hypothesize, conjecture, guess	Confirm, ascertain, verify	S	9
477	make laws, enact legislation, pass laws	repeal, abolish, annul	L	9
478	prohibit, forbid, bar	allow, permit	B	3
479	relapse, deteriorate, revert	progress, advance	R	7
480	fantastic, excellent, wonderful	awful, terrible	T	8

Day 13

번호	영어	한글
481	A rather than B	
482	propel	
483	dismiss	
484	inhale	
485	hoop	
486	commentary	
487	trace	
488	query	
489	neglect	
490	infer	
491	ascribe	
492	minister	
493	away from	
494	array	
495	catastrophe	
496	ignoble	
497	have a point	
498	kindle	
499	compound	
500	fiery	

* 유의어와 반의어에 '0'이 있는 문제는 해당 어휘가 없는 경우이니 그냥 패스하시면 됩니다. 글자수의 (p.)는 '숙어' 표시입니다.

번호	유의어	반의어	영어	글자수
501	vast, enormous, colossal	small, tiny	I	7
502	step, walk, pace	Stagnation, standstill, immobility	S	6
503	unused, undeveloped, unexplored	Utilized, exploited, harnessed	U	8
504	frugality, economy, thriftiness	Waste, extravagance, prodigality	T	6
505	clear, apparent, evident	hidden, concealed	O	7
506	independence, self-rule, sovereignty	dependence, subordination, reliance	A	8
507	handle, use, exercise	relinquish, surrender, abandon	W	5
508	similar, alike, cut from the same mold	different, dissimilar, unrelated	C	19 (p.)
509	apologize for, justify oneself for, offer an explanation for	blame oneself for, condemn oneself for, criticize oneself for	E	16 (p.)
510	crave, desire, long	despise, loathe, detest	Y	5
511	stitch, stitch up, mend	rip, tear	S	3
512	conversely, however	on the same side, likewise	O	13 (p.)
513	coincide, correspond with	differ from, be unrelated to	C	12 (p.)
514	control, influence, maneuver	leave untouched, keep intact, preserve	M	10
515	discard A, disregard A, dismiss A	retain A, keep A, embrace A	C	10 (p.)
516	aid, assist, help	abandon one, desert one, neglect one	C	17 (p.)
517	encourage, motivate, stimulate	Delay, hesitation, procrastination	P	6
518	accomplish, achieve, complete	disappoint, fail	F	7
519	be subjected to, be vulnerable to	be protected from, shielded from	B	11 (p.)
520	captivate, bewitch, charm	repel, disgust	E	7

Day 14

번호	영어	한글
521	strike a deal	
522	parallel	
523	go with	
524	fraud	
525	exploit	
526	coverage	
527	subtract	
528	doctrine	
529	segment	
530	allot	
531	anonymous	
532	exaggerate	
533	consent	
534	at most	
535	inflow	
536	ambiguous	
537	fierce	
538	occupy	
539	bury	
540	occur to N	

* 유의어와 반의어에 '0'이 있는 문제는 해당 어휘가 없는 경우이니 그냥 패스하시면 됩니다. 글자수의 (p.)는 '숙어' 표시입니다.

번호	유의어	반의어	영어	글자수
541	corrupt, payoff, inducement	Legal payment, authorized compensation, legitimate reward	B	5
542	compliant, submissive, dutiful	Disobedient, rebellious, defiant	O	8
543	outdated, obsolete, old-fashioned	up-to-date, current, modern	O	9 (p.)
544	brutality, aggression, force	Non-violence, peace, non-aggression	V	8
545	pant, wheeze, breathe heavily	breathe, exhale	G	4
546	in accordance with, in sync with	in conflict with, discordant with	I	13 (p.)
547	central to, core of, essence of	peripheral to, away from, on the outskirts of	A	12 (p.)
548	main, principal, chief	Secondary, auxiliary, subordinate	P	7
549	retract, pull back, remove	deposit, contribute, add	W	8
550	overpower, overcome, inundate	underwhelm, fail to impress, disappoint	O	9
551	no matter what, regardless of the expense, by any means necessary	at no cost, at no expense, without any sacrifice	A	10 (p.)
552	distance, range, extent from center	Diameter, width, breadth	R	6
553	qualified, suitable, entitled	Ineligible, disqualified, unqualified	E	8
554	grasp, understand, comprehend	lose understanding of, be confused about, misunderstand	G	12 (p.)
555	enumeration, population count, survey	Non-census, non-enumeration, non-count	C	6
556	temperate, reasonable, middle-of-the-road	extreme, excessive, immoderate	M	8
557	path, trajectory, course	Standstill, halt, stationary	O	5
558	afraid of, frightened of, fearful of	unafraid of, fearless of, courageous in the face of	B	10 (p.)
559	gather, amass, collect	Disperse, scatter, spread out	A	10
560	disappear, fade, evaporate	Appear, materialize, emerge	V	6

Day 15

번호	영어	한글
561	swell	
562	in a degree	
563	compulsive	
564	far from	
565	attempt	
566	glide	
567	irrespective	
568	assure	
569	stockpile	
570	implement	
571	resolute	
572	honour A with B	
573	hypothesis	
574	conform	
575	congress	
576	courteous	
577	in awe of	
578	derive	
579	carpenter	
580	be founded on	

* 유의어와 반의어에 '0'이 있는 문제는 해당 어휘가 없는 경우이니 그냥 패스하시면 됩니다. 글자수의 (p.)는 '숙어' 표시입니다.

번호	유의어	반의어	영어	글자수
581	accommodate, make room for	prohibit, disallow	A	8 (p.)
582	provided with, furnished with, supplied with	lacking, devoid of, unprepared for	E	12 (p.)
583	repress, quell, inhibit	express, reveal, display	S	8
584	forbid, ban, disallow	permit, allow	P	8
585	strive, endeavor, exert	ease, breeze, cakewalk	S	8
586	celebrate, honor, remember	forget, neglect, ignore	C	11
587	focus, obsess, concentrate	release, free, liberate	F	6
588	captivate, enchant, bewitch	bore, repel	F	9
589	begin, start, commence	conclude, finish, terminate	I	8
590	considering A, bearing A in consideration	without A in mind, absent A	W	11 (p.)
591	complexify, entangle, confuse	simplify, clarify	C	10
592	crowd, mass, throng	Few, handful, limited number	M	9
593	obstinate, inflexible, unyielding	flexible, pliable	S	8
594	embark on, tackle, take on	abandon, give up, relinquish	U	9
595	cut in half, divide by two, split	double, increase, multiply	H	5
596	hug, cuddle, clasp	reject, push away	E	7
597	resistance, disobedience, rebellion	submission, obedience, compliance	D	8
598	for that purpose, with that aim, in order to achieve that	aimlessly, purposelessly, without intention	T	9 (p.)
599	material, matter, stuff	Nothingness, nonentity, void	S	9
600	true, accurate, real	Unfactual, false, fictional	F	7

Day 16

번호	영어	한글
601	insomnia	
602	alienation	
603	take after	
604	innate	
605	at peace	
606	greed	
607	nominate	
608	withhold	
609	eliminate	
610	outweigh	
611	weird	
612	repute	
613	catch up on	
614	causal	
615	be subjected to N	
616	superstition	
617	from above	
618	assassinate	
619	peel	
620	mature	

* 유의어와 반의어에 '0'이 있는 문제는 해당 어휘가 없는 경우이니 그냥 패스하시면 됩니다. 글자수의 (p.)는 '숙어' 표시입니다.

번호	유의어	반의어	영어	글자수
621	supplementary, additional, matching	Non-complementary, non-matching, mismatched	C	10
622	outline, profile, contour	detail, elaboration, intricacy	S	10
623	feed, sustain, nurture	starve, deprive, neglect	N	7
624	stressed, anxious, nervous	relaxed, calm	T	5
625	deteriorating, decreasing, waning	improving, rising, advancing	I	9 (p.)
626	at the start of, initially, in the early stages of	at the end of, in the middle of, midway through	A	16 (p.)
627	overweight, corpulence, heaviness	thinness, slenderness, leanness	O	7
628	advantageous to, beneficial to, in one's favor	against one's interest, to one's detriment, disadvantageously	I	15 (p.)
629	pole, spar, sail support	Bow, front, prow	M	4
630	walker, foot-traveler, walker	Driver, motorist, commuter	P	10
631	link with, associate with	disconnect from, detach from	C	11 (p.)
632	discard, get rid of, eliminate	acquire, obtain, keep	D	9 (p.)
633	hold, grip, seize	release, let go, surrender	G	5
634	suffocate, submerge, immerse	Save, rescue, survive	D	5
635	heartbreaking, sorrowful, lamentable	fortunate, joyful	T	6
636	starvation, scarcity of food, hunger crisis	Abundance, plenty, surplus	F	6
637	boy, youth, youngster	girl, lass	L	3
638	endorse, support, agree with	disapprove of, reject, oppose	A	9 (p.)
639	swing, influence, control	stabilize, balance, steady	S	4
640	be related to, be associated with, be connected to	unrelated to, disconnected from, irrelevant to	H	21 (p.)

Day 17

번호	영어	한글
641	prefer A to B	
642	near at hand	
643	admiral	
644	by way of	
645	cosmopolitan	
646	linear	
647	immune to N	
648	timely	
649	obtain	
650	caught in	
651	be obligated to do	
652	captive	
653	perspiration	
654	retail	
655	spur	
656	communism	
657	in contact with	
658	in common with	
659	stance	
660	give a hand	

TEST

* 유의어와 반의어에 '0'이 있는 문제는 해당 어휘가 없는 경우이니 그냥 패스하시면 됩니다. 글자수의 (p.)는 '숙어' 표시입니다.

번호	유의어	반의어	영어	글자수
661	realize, become aware, snap out of it	remain unaware, continue unaware, overlook	C	12 (p.)
662	produce, make, fabricate	Unmake, disassemble, break down	M	11
663	favored by, popular with	out of favor with, unpopular with	I	11 (p.)
664	expel, oust, remove	admit, allow, welcome	E	5
665	earnings, income, gain	Loss, deficit, financial loss	P	6
666	massive, huge, colossal	tiny, small	E	8
667	be inclined to do, tend to do, have a tendency to do	be unlikely to do, rarely do, seldom do	B	11 (p.)
668	status, reputation, standing	Disrepute, disesteem, lack of respect	P	8
669	imperil, jeopardize, threaten	protect, safeguard	E	8
670	uneducated, unlettered, non-literate	Literate, educated, knowledgeable	I	10
671	register, sign up, join	Unenroll, withdraw, drop out	E	6
672	fissure, split, fracture	Seal, close, mend	C	5
673	undernourishment, poor nutrition, starvation	nourishment, nutrition, health	M	12
674	group, bunch, collection	Disperse, scatter, separate	C	7
675	traditional stories, legends, oral history	Modern culture, contemporary traditions, current customs	F	8
676	hollow, hole, void	Solidity, density, compactness	C	6
677	empathy, sympathy, kindness	indifference, cruelty	C	10
678	confess, acknowledge, concede	deny, reject	A	5
679	grasp, seize, take control	release, let go, relinquish	T	8 (p.)
680	burning, ignition, combustion process	Extinguishment, quenching, dousing	C	10

53

Day 18

번호	영어	한글
681	committee	
682	inquire	
683	expend	
684	janitor	
685	stout	
686	barn	
687	execute	
688	hereby	
689	commend	
690	distinguish	
691	at latest	
692	subordinate	
693	in a timely fashion	
694	enlist	
695	come of age	
696	deed	
697	cut off	
698	a great deal of	
699	paralyze	
700	thorn	

* 유의어와 반의어에 'O'이 있는 문제는 해당 어휘가 없는 경우이니 그냥 패스하시면 됩니다. 글자수의 (p.)는 '숙어' 표시입니다.

번호	유의어	반의어	영어	글자수
701	fixate, preoccupy, haunt	detach, disconnect	O	6
702	authorize, justify, permit	Forbid, prohibit, disallow	W	7
703	hunger, famish, deprive of food	Overeat, indulge, overindulge	S	6
704	be segmented into, be separated into	be united into, merge together	B	13 (p.)
705	selective, restricted, limited to few	Inclusive, open, accessible	E	9
706	plan, strategy, plot	honesty, sincerity	S	6
707	compress, reduce, concentrate	Expand, dilate, inflate	C	8
708	calmness, tranquility, poise	agitation, anxiety, restlessness	C	9
709	harmonious, agreeable, compatible	Vowel, non-consonant, non-vocalic	C	9
710	expect, predict, foresee	overlook, disregard, ignore	A	10
711	magic, sorcery, transformation	Chemistry, science, natural philosophy	A	7
712	desire, impulse, prompt	discourage, dissuade	U	4
713	graveyard, burial ground, necropolis	birthplace, cradle, beginning	C	8
714	adapt to N, acclimatize to N	resist N, oppose N	A	9 (p.)
715	biology, study of the body, bodily functions	Anatomy, morphology, bodily structure	P	10
716	creep, slither, inch	sprint, rush	C	5
717	being considered, on the table	disregarded, ignored	U	18 (p.)
718	representative, envoy, proxy	Retain, keep, hold onto	D	8
719	confirm, validate, authenticate	refute, disprove, debunk	V	6
720	endure, bear, withstand	reject, resist	T	8

Day 19

번호	영어	한글
721	accord	
722	on the surface	
723	by turns	
724	oppress	
725	recognize	
726	appear to do	
727	shorthand	
728	at a discount	
729	realty	
730	severe	
731	sake	
732	in partnership with	
733	constrict	
734	cope with	
735	deficit	
736	correspond	
737	discharge	
738	deposit	
739	scarcity	
740	thrust	

* 유의어와 반의어에 'O'이 있는 문제는 해당 어휘가 없는 경우이니 그냥 패스하시면 됩니다. 글자수의 (p.)는 '숙어' 표시입니다.

번호	유의어	반의어	영어	글자수
741	impartial, unbiased, uninvolved	Biased, prejudiced, partial	N	7
742	veneration, adoration, reverence	Desecrate, profane, blaspheme	W	7
743	achieve, reach, accomplish	Lose, fail, surrender	A	6
744	contemplate, reflect, ponder	agitate, disturb	M	8
745	abuse, mistreat, mishandle	proper use, correct usage, appropriate application	M	6
746	heavenly, godly, sacred	Human, earthly, mortal	D	6
747	successive, sequential, in a row	Non-consecutive, sporadic, intermittent	C	11
748	trend, craze, fashion	Permanence, long-lasting trend, sustained fashion	F	3
749	mumble, whisper, mutter	shout, yell	M	6
750	in childhood, when young, from a young age	in later life, in adulthood, in maturity	A	12 (p.)
751	element, part, ingredient	Whole, entirety, complete entity	C	9
752	taste, seasoning, savor	Tastelessness, blandness, lack of flavor	F	6
753	rude, discourteous, disrespectful	Polite, courteous, well-mannered	I	8
754	be proud of, pride oneself on, feel proud about	be ashamed of, be embarrassed by, be humiliated by	T	11 (p.)
755	contradiction, puzzle, enigma	Consistency, agreement, conformity	P	7
756	fierce, extreme, concentrated	mild, gentle	I	7
757	minimize, de-emphasize, understress	emphasize, highlight, stress	D	8
758	suffocate, stifle, suppress	uncover, reveal	S	7
759	portion, part, segment	Whole, entirety, complete entity	F	8
760	encounter, stumble upon	avoid, bypass	C	10 (p.)

Day 20

번호	영어	한글
761	boredom	
762	reveal	
763	convince	
764	fling	
765	hygiene	
766	fur	
767	profound	
768	requisite	
769	fall on	
770	advent	
771	confine	
772	protest	
773	sewage	
774	ripe	
775	statistics	
776	set in one's way	
777	one after another	
778	dense	
779	tuition	
780	all the more	

TEST

' 유의어와 반의어에 '0'이 있는 문제는 해당 어휘가 없는 경우이니 그냥 패스하시면 됩니다. 글자수의 (p.)는 '숙어' 표시입니다.

번호	유의어	반의어	영어	글자수
781	region, district, administrative division	City, municipality, metropolis	C	6
782	behavior, demeanor, performance	misbehave, behave badly, transgress	C	7
783	excellent, outstanding, splendid	awful, poor	S	6
784	know, be acquainted with, recognize	be unfamiliar with, be ignorant of, be unaware of	B	14 (p.)
785	imitate, copy, emulate	Original, genuine, authentic	M	5
786	commit, devote, consecrate	abandon, forsake	D	8
787	pair A with B, match A to B, combine A and B	disconnect A from B, separate A from B, decouple A from B	C	12 (p.)
788	allocate, dispense, apportion	collect, hoard	D	10
789	authentic, real, true	Fake, counterfeit, phony	G	7
790	direct, simple, uncomplicated	complicated, complex	S	15
791	mention, quote, reference	omit, disregard, ignore	C	4
792	empty, clear, purge	fill, stock, replenish	C	8 (p.)
793	cry out, shout, declare	whisper, mumble, mutter	E	7
794	by this time, at this point, already	until now, up until this point, hitherto	B	5 (p.)
795	misfortune, accident, bad luck	Fortune, luck, success	M	9
796	beginning, start, commencement	Conclusion, end, termination	O	6
797	weak, feeble, faint-hearted	strong, bold	F	5
798	sufficient, enough, ample	insufficient, inadequate, lacking	A	8
799	similarly, likewise, in a similar manner	differently, dissimilarly, disparately	I	12 (p.)
800	study, cram, revise	skip studying, ignore the books, neglect learning	H	11 (p.)

' 유의어와 반의어에 '0'이 있는 문제는 해당 어휘가 없는 경우이니 그냥 패스하시면 됩니다. 글자수의 (p.)는 '숙어' 표시입니다.

Day 21

번호	영어	한글
801	affect	
802	as to	
803	armament	
804	fortify	
805	exquisite	
806	affair	
807	prosper	
808	what is more	
809	pioneer	
810	numerous	
811	proportion	
812	in any case	
813	craft	
814	go off	
815	indulge	
816	proclaim	
817	epidemic	
818	recover from	
819	be fond of	
820	commitment to N	

* 유의어와 반의어에 '0'이 있는 문제는 해당 어휘가 없는 경우이니 그냥 패스하시면 됩니다. 글자수의 (p.)는 '숙어' 표시입니다.

번호	유의어	반의어	영어	글자수
821	in line with, compatible with, congruent with	conflicting with, contradictory to, incompatible with	C	14 (p.)
822	discussion, conversation, dialogue	silence, quietude, muteness	D	9
823	murder, killing, manslaughter	Survival, non-killing, non-murder	H	8
824	without, lacking	in the presence of, with	I	14 (p.)
825	ethical, virtuous, righteous	Immoral, unethical, corrupt	M	5
826	disagree with, object to, take issue with	agree with, accept, support	H	16 (p.)
827	convent, abbey, cloister	secular, non-religious, worldly	M	9
828	ten years, decennium, decagon	century, millennium	D	6
829	shrivel, wilt, fade	Thrive, flourish, bloom	W	6
830	calm, comfort, pacify	agitate, disturb	S	6
831	draw A to B, entice A towards B, lure A to B	repel A from B, deter A from B, discourage A from B	A	11 (p.)
832	compute, estimate, figure	guess, estimate, conjecture	C	9
833	include, integrate, merge	Exclude, eliminate, omit	I	11
834	associated with, linked to, connected with	unrelated to, independent of, unconnected to	C	14 (p.)
835	devise, concoct, think of	fail to produce, lack creativity, be unoriginal	C	10 (p.)
836	depict, represent, portray	obscure, hide	R	6
837	plants, flora, greenery	Barrenness, desolation, aridness	V	10
838	pressure gauge, weather indicator, atmospheric instrument	Irrelevant, unimportant, insignificant	B	9
839	remove A, extract A, take A out	put A in, place A inside, insert A	G	7 (p.)
840	sadden, dishearten, demoralize	elevate, uplift, raise	D	7

Day 22

번호	영어	한글
841	work out	
842	punctuate	
843	contribution	
844	cut out	
845	merchant	
846	get around	
847	moan	
848	capitalize on	
849	profess	
850	foe	
851	impulse	
852	indicate	
853	ascend	
854	favoritism	
855	hand down	
856	hostility	
857	equator	
858	contaminate	
859	curb	
860	lament	

ᴗ 유의어와 반의어에 '0'이 있는 문제는 해당 어휘가 없는 경우이니 그냥 패스하시면 됩니다. 글자수의 (p.)는 '숙어' 표시입니다.

번호	유의어	반의어	영어	글자수
861	vote, election, polling	Dictatorship, autocracy, one-person rule	B	6
862	quit, step down, retire	Accept, embrace, take on	R	6
863	unemotional, detached, objective	Personal, individual, subjective	I	10
864	enforce A on B, compel B to accept A, thrust A upon B	liberate B from A, free B from A, release B from A	I	10 (p.)
865	harvest, gather, collect	sow, plant	R	4
866	settlement, outpost, territory	Homeland, native land, motherland	C	6
867	courteous, polite, kind	discourteous, impolite, rude	G	8
868	cause, induce, generate	prevent, hinder, impede	B	10 (p.)
869	towards each other, to one another, facing each other	apart from one another, separate from one another, isolated from one another	A	12 (p.)
870	discomfort, anxiety, apprehension	comfort, ease, tranquility	U	6
871	merchandise, goods, products	Empty, vacant, bare	W	4
872	notice, discern, detect	overlook, miss	P	8
873	happen, occur	cease, stop	C	9 (p.)
874	arrange, adjust, coordinate	misalign, disarrange	A	5
875	investigator, sleuth, private eye	Criminal, wrongdoer, perpetrator	D	9
876	immerse, plunge, submerse	Emerge, surface, appear	S	8
877	allude to, mention, cite	disregard N, ignore N, overlook N	R	8 (p.)
878	fall, trip, topple	stand, rise, ascend	T	6
879	legitimate, acceptable, lawful	Invalid, void, null	V	5
880	innate, intrinsic, natural	acquired, learned	I	8

Day 23

번호	영어	한글
881	mob	
882	solvent	
883	so long as	
884	steer	
885	disturb	
886	lunar	
887	associate	
888	depict	
889	conceal	
890	interfere	
891	diffuse	
892	confuse A with B	
893	cut down on	
894	coward	
895	as we speak	
896	hibernate	
897	nurture	
898	at the moment	
899	at one's convenience	
900	celsius	

TEST

* 유의어와 반의어에 'O'이 있는 문제는 해당 어휘가 없는 경우이니 그냥 패스하시면 됩니다. 글자수의 (p.)는 '숙어' 표시입니다.

번호	유의어	반의어	영어	글자수
901	exclude, skip, leave out	include, add, incorporate	O	4
902	provoke, irritate, agitate	soothe, calm	I	7
903	casket, burial box, sarcophagus	cradle, crib, bassinet	C	6
904	cut up, slice, dice	assemble, construct, build	C	6 (p.)
905	say, speak, articulate	withhold, retain, keep	U	5
906	private, secret, classified	public, open	C	12
907	strengthen, fortify, bolster	weaken, undermine	R	9
908	break, fracture, smash	mend, repair	S	7
909	involve, participate, commit	disengage, withdraw, detach	E	6
910	receive from, be left with, acquire through inheritance	disinherit, deprive of inheritance, exclude from inheritance	I	11 (p.)
911	enough, adequate, ample	Insufficient, inadequate, lacking	S	10
912	an amount of, a number of, a volume of	a lack of, an absence of, a scarcity of	A	11 (p.)
913	connection, interaction, linkage	disconnect, separate	I	9
914	foreign, unusual, unfamiliar	Familiar, common, ordinary	E	6
915	area, region, locality	Central, main, city center	D	8
916	adjust to N, acclimate to N	resist N, oppose N	A	8 (p.)
917	deluge, flood, downpour	Drought, dry spell, aridity	T	7
918	uncertain, unresolved, pending	certain, definite, resolved	I	8 (p.)
919	eliminate, abolish, eradicate	keep, maintain, retain	D	10 (p.)
920	apathetic, uninterested, uncaring	concerned, interested, caring	I	11

Day 24

번호	영어	한글
921	strive for	
922	break in	
923	with access to	
924	commence	
925	assume	
926	deluxe	
927	flock	
928	convert	
929	undermine	
930	persist in	
931	bygone	
932	curse	
933	gloomy	
934	endeavor	
935	tin	
936	distract	
937	metabolic	
938	account for	
939	obstruct	
940	legacy	

* 유의어와 반의어에 '0'이 있는 문제는 해당 어휘가 없는 경우이니 그냥 패스하시면 됩니다. 글자수의 (p.)는 '숙어' 표시입니다.

번호	유의어	반의어	영어	글자수
941	order, series, arrangement	Disarray, randomness, chaos	S	8
942	die, expire, pass away	thrive, flourish, endure	P	6
943	determine, decide, settle	hesitate, waver	R	7
944	verbal, language-related, lexical	non-linguistic, non-verbal, a-linguistic	L	10
945	vanished, eradicated, no longer existing	Alive, living, existing	E	7
946	careless, irresponsible, thoughtless	cautious, prudent, careful	R	8
947	adhere, stick, hold on	release, let go	C	5
948	expectant, with child, in the family way	barren, infertile, childless	P	8
949	demonstrate, reveal, display	hide, conceal	M	8
950	ambition, goal, desire	Resignation, acceptance, contentment	A	10
951	grieve, lament, weep for	celebrate, rejoice, be happy	M	5
952	assign, delegate, hand over	withhold, retain, keep	E	7
953	conflict, discord, disagreement	Harmony, peace, tranquility	S	6
954	send, transmit, convey	receive, accept, take in	D	8
955	derive, obtain, draw out	Insert, replace, put in	E	7
956	begin to do, start to do, undertake	avoid doing, refrain from doing, eschew doing	C	8 (p.)
957	deplete, drain, wear out	refresh, rejuvenate, energize	E	7
958	sometimes, occasionally, from time to time	consistently, constantly, continually	A	7 (p.)
959	agree with, comply with, conform to	oppose, disagree with, resist	G	11 (p.)
960	risk, danger, peril	safety, security, certainty	H	6

Day 25

번호	영어	한글
961	lyric	
962	deal with	
963	disrupt	
964	observe	
965	embarrass	
966	quotation	
967	critical	
968	thread	
969	successive	
970	segregation	
971	be to blame for	
972	demand	
973	forbid	
974	ruthless	
975	assemble	
976	in conclusion	
977	infrastructure	
978	altitude	
979	frigid	
980	testify	

* 유의어와 반의어에 '0'이 있는 문제는 해당 어휘가 없는 경우이니 그냥 패스하시면 됩니다. 글자수의 (p.)는 '숙어' 표시입니다.

번호	유의어	반의어	영어	글자수
981	impress, amaze, astound	disappoint, underwhelm, bore	B	8 (p.)
982	consider, meditate, reflect	neglect, disregard	C	11
983	sincerely, genuinely, honestly	in bad faith, dishonestly, deceitfully	I	11 (p.)
984	thoughtlessly, without thinking, automatically	consciously, purposefully, deliberately	M	10
985	incidentally, casually	deliberately, purposefully	I	9 (p.)
986	always, constantly, continuously	never, seldom, rarely	A	10 (p.)
987	chute, descent device, skydiving equipment	Fall, drop, descend	P	9
988	stress, tension, pressure	ease, relax	S	6
989	look like, mirror, simulate	differ, contrast, deviate	R	8
990	be familiar with N, be used to N	be unaccustomed to N, unfamiliar with N	B	15 (p.)
991	unavoidable, certain, inescapable	Avoidable, preventable, escapable	I	10
992	peak, pinnacle, zenith	Bottom, base, nadir	S	6
993	unbiased, neutral, fair	Biased, prejudiced, unfair	I	9
994	moderate, mild, restrained	extreme, excessive, immoderate	T	9
995	control, overpower, rule	submit, yield	D	8
996	post facto, retrospectively, after the event	before the fact, pre-emptively, beforehand	A	12 (p.)
997	relinquish, transfer	withhold, keep	H	8 (p.)
998	good, product, item	luxury, rarity, uniqueness	C	9
999	ideal, best, optimal	suboptimal, inferior	O	7
1000	declare, claim, state	deny, disclaim, negate	A	6

Answers.

Day 1		Day 2		Day 3		Day 4	

page 4 · page 7 · page 10 · page 13

번호	정답	번호	정답	번호	정답	번호	정답
1	a. 우울한, 슬픈	41	a. 더러운, 불결한, 불순한	81	v. ~을 제한하다, 금지하다, 한정하다	121	p. 소위, 말하자면
2	a. 어두운, 분명치 않은	42	a. 예민한, 신중한, 매우 관심이 많은; 깊은, 강한	82	p. ~하려는 노력으로	122	v. 조직화하다, 조정하다
3	p. 대개, 흔히	43	p. 물러나다, (하기로 했던 일에서) 빠지다	83	a. 괴짜인, 별난	123	v. 당황하게 하다
4	v. A를 세우다, A를 정지시키다	44	p. ~이 아니게 되다	84	v. ~로 병합하다, ~에 융합하다	124	v. 배수하다, 물을 빼내다
5	n. 용량, 능력, 수용력	45	a. 최대의, 극도의	85	n. 큰 슬픔	125	n. 혜성
6	a. 풍자적인, 빈정대는; 비꼬는	46	v. 주관하다, 주재하다	86	n. 특권, 특전	126	a. 양자택일의 n. 양자택일, (보통 복수형)
7	v. 출발하다	47	n. 연민, 동정, 유감	87	v. 기르다, 함양하다, 재배하다; 계발하다	127	v. 망치다, 파산시키다; 파산, 붕괴
8	v. A를 B 중심으로[B에 맞춰] 조절하다	48	v. 불모의, 황량한	88	n. 놀라운 일 v. 놀라다	128	a. 적당한, 타당한
9	a. 지켜보는, 주의 깊은	49	v. 결정하다, 측정하다, 판정하다	89	p. ~에 속하다	129	v. 조심하다, 주의하다
10	p. 공짜로	50	n. 포도나무, 덩굴 식물	90	p. ~에 잘 들어맞다, 적합하다	130	p. 외워서
11	v. 가까워지다, 근접하다 a. 근사치의, 대략적인	51	v. 지속하다, 견디다	91	v. 돌이켜보다, 추억하다; 추억, 회상	131	a. 기운이 없는, 다리를 절다, 절뚝거림
12	n. 결점, 문제점	52	v. 빛을 비추다, 밝히다	92	n. 멍, 타박상	132	n. 몸매를 가꾸다
13	v. 거절하다, 사절하다	53	vi. (문제 상황이) 일어나다, 발생하다	93	v. 끄다, 소멸시키다	133	n. 접미사
14	a. 두드러진, 우세한, 지배적인	54	a. 신경의	94	n. 종족(로마제국의 3종족에서 유래)	134	v. 왜곡하다; 바꾸다, 비틀다
15	v. 중재하다, 개입하다	55	v. (방향을) 전환하다	95	p. 계속 수행하다, 계속 ~하다	135	v. 완전히 파괴하다, 유린하다, 황폐화하다
16	p. ~을 두려워하지, 겁내다	56	p. ~에 반응하다	96	a. 또렷한, 명백한, 외견상의, 겉보기에는	136	a. 전체의, 건강에 좋은, 건전한
17	v. 대체하다, 바꾸다; 대신하다	57	a. 돌출한; 눈에 띄는, 탁월한	97	n. 떨림, 전율; v. (몸을) 떨다	137	n. 성명, 성명서; 명세서; 진술, 연설
18	v. 파내다, 발굴하다; 밝혀 내다	58	n. 퇴비, 두엄 v. 퇴비를 만들다	98	p. 시작하다, [계약 따위를] 맺다	138	a. 합법의, 적법의
19	n. 입장, 견지, 관점	59	a. 이국풍의, 색다른, 이상한, 기이한	99	a. 솔직한, 숨김없는, 명백한, 공정한	139	v. 인정하다, 시인하다; 고백하다
20	v. ~에 열중하다, 몰두하다	60	p. ~이라는 것을 고려하면	100	v. 비난하다; 선고하다	140	v. 쓸모가 있다, 도움이 되다

page 5 · page 8 · page 11 · page 14

번호	정답	번호	정답	번호	정답	번호	정답
21	scent	61	compel	101	mutual	141	hardwire
22	abundant	62	alliance	102	inhibit	142	predator
23	seizure	63	outright	103	have an impact on	143	outdo
24	accurate	64	patron	104	prone	144	fragile
25	none the worse	65	surplus	105	get along with	145	be attached to
26	on one's feet	66	esteem	106	expel	146	plural
27	dissolve	67	persevere	107	reed	147	compact
28	haste	68	inhabit	108	digest	148	invert
29	remark	69	accentuate	109	constitution	149	be conscious of
30	deflect	70	disinterested	110	in the way	150	prolong
31	indebt	71	taboo	111	flush	151	overthrow
32	flatter	72	significant	112	proficient	152	notable
33	be subject to N	73	at a charge of	113	geometry	153	archery
34	frustrate	74	have a handle on	114	deter	154	feed on
35	possess	75	imply	115	elaborate	155	backfire
36	damaging to N	76	chances are	116	anecdote	156	terminate
37	magnetism	77	bald	117	restore	157	adore
38	fabulous	78	comprise	118	mash	158	wreckage
39	allocate	79	pursue	119	specimen	159	parliament
40	sumptuous	80	tempt	120	cruel	160	erect

Day 5		Day 6		Day 7		Day 8	

page 16 · page 19 · page 22 · page 25

번호	정답	번호	정답	번호	정답	번호	정답
161	v. 논쟁하다, 토론하다 n. 논쟁	201	n. (울타리로 쳐 놓은) 구역	241	n. (작은 보트의) 노, 주걱	281	p. ~의 의지에 반하여 행동하다
162	n. 기둥; 기념비; (신문) 칼럼	202	v. ~에서 벗어난	242	v. 줄어들다	282	p. 그림을 그리다; ~에 의존하다
163	a. 제국의, 황제의	203	v. 재채기를 하다	243	n. 멈춤, 중단 v. 멈추다, 서다	283	p. 취소하다, 중지하다
164	n. 선박; 혈관; 용기	204	v. 흐느껴 울다	244	n. 얼룩; v. 마구 바르다, 더럽히다	284	n. 양심, 도덕심
165	a. 황량한, 쓸쓸한	205	n. 수입, 세입, 세수	245	v. 얼굴을 붉히다, 빨개지다	285	n. 나루터, 나룻배, 연락선 v. 수송하다
166	v. 고장이 나다	206	v. 끄덕이다, (고개를) 까딱하다	246	v. 거주하다, 살다	286	v. 단념하다, 포기하다, 버리다
167	v. 나오다, 등장하다	207	p. ~을 넘어서다, ~을 지나가다	247	a. 열의, 보온성이 좋은	287	v. 문지르다
168	a. 힘이 없는, 무기력한	208	v. 상처 입히다, 다치게 하다	248	p. ~을 이용하다	288	p. A와 B를 통합시키다
169	v. 제출하다	209	a. 한심한, 형편없는; 애처로운	249	p. A를 당연하게 여기다	289	a. 중세의 [ev 시대(age)]
170	p. (주장 등을) 굽히다, 양보하다	210	a. 신속한, 빠른	250	a. 엄숙한, 침통한	290	v. 단열 처리를 하다, 방음 처리를 하다
171	n. 희생; 제물 v. 희생하다, 바치다	211	v. 환대, 후한 대접	251	a. 심미적, 미학적, 미적인	291	a. 확실한, 확고한, 분명한
172	v. 줄이다	212	p. ~할 여유가 있다, ~할 수 있다	252	p. ~을 따라 이름 짓다	292	n. 격노, 격한 분노
173	p. 반값 할인	213	n. 비관론자, 염세주의자	253	p. ~을 무시위하다	293	a. 묵살하려다, 간과하다
174	v. 깜짝 놀라게 하다	214	v. 번식하다; 새끼를 낳다; 사육하다, 재배하다	254	n. 많은 사람들이 알고 있는 사람, 명성	294	v. 퇴화하다, 퇴보하다, 타락하다
175	v. ~에 호소하다	215	n. 군주제, 군주국, 군주 일가, 왕가	255	p. ~에도 불구하고, ~에 직면하여	295	a. 초보의, 초급의, 기본적인
176	n. 신경, 긴장, 불안	216	v. 바느질하다; 바늘땀, 코, 바느질	256	v. 달성하다, 이루어 내다	296	v. 살금살금 가다, 몰래 가다
177	v. 달래다, 위로하다	217	v. 주장하다; 요구하다	257	n. 사랑, 박애, 관용; 자선(행위), 자선(단체)	297	v. 짜증나게 하다; (피부 등을) 자극하다
178	a. 말의, 문자 그대로의	218	p. 잇달아, 연이어	258	a. 책임을 져야 할, ~ 경향이 있는, ~하기 쉬운	298	a. 당의(설탕을 입힌 과자)
179	a. 누적되는, 가중의	219	n. 연회, 만찬	259	v. (결과·이익 등을) 내다, 생산하다; 항복하다	299	n. 담보물, 인질
180	a. 습한, 습기가 있는	220	v. 반박하다	260	n. 규정, 조항, 공급, 대비	300	a. 싫어하는, 꺼리는

page 17 · page 20 · page 23 · page 26

번호	정답	번호	정답	번호	정답	번호	정답
181	reflect	221	take in	261	by law	301	shed
182	council	222	exile	262	go for	302	evacuate
183	discriminate	223	have only to do	263	deduction	303	fundamental
184	get into trouble	224	fatigue	264	intimate	304	have a taste for
185	crater	225	heritage	265	trim	305	synthetic
186	in one's opinion	226	get A out of the way	266	have a discussion with	306	demerit
187	irrational	227	on one's own	267	criterion	307	raid
188	be capable of	228	in the long run	268	awkward	308	abstract
189	around the clock	229	ultraviolet	269	cognitive	309	potential
190	undo	230	potable	270	cold to N	310	hold together
191	against the laws	231	magnificent	271	affirm	311	reservoir
192	in the coming year	232	deliberate	272	chronic	312	corrupt
193	atmosphere	233	live beyond one's income	273	harsh	313	enact
194	hold on	234	dehydrate	274	deprive A of B	314	stain
195	in consultation with	235	compass	275	portray	315	infection
196	acknowledge	236	stationary	276	rear	316	at a low price
197	emerge	237	a majority of	277	catholic	317	vulnerable to N
198	in the mood for	238	table of contents	278	except for	318	owe A to B
199	impair	239	entail	279	velocity	319	for a change
200	vital	240	precise	280	qualified to do	320	peer

Day 9 / Day 10 / Day 11 / Day 12

번호	정답 (page 28)	번호	정답 (page 31)	번호	정답 (page 34)	번호	정답 (page 37)
321	p. ~한 가격으로	361	n. 불행, 고통, 비참(함)	401	n. 규율, 통제, 학문, 기강, 훈련	441	a. 매우 귀중한
322	p. ~을 두려워하다, ~을 경외하다	362	v. 보험에 들다	402	p. 적어도	442	p. ~하는데 어려움을 겪다
323	p. 선호하는 일, 기호[취미]에 맞는 일	363	v. ~과 반대의	403	a. ~에 열중하고 있는	443	v. 근절하다, 박멸하다
324	n. 직관, 직관력, 통찰력	364	v. 패배시키다, 좌절시키다	404	a. 절망적인, 자포자기의, 무모한; 필사적인	444	a. 양립할 수 있는, 조화되는; 호환되는
325	p. 성급하게 결론을 내리다	365	v. 유지하다; 부상을 입다; 지지하다; 부양하다	405	p. 최신 정보를 계속 유지하다	445	n. 넝마 조각, 누더기 옷
326	v. 동원하다	366	p. ~에 근거하다	406	a. 버림받은, 쫓겨난, 버림받은 사람	446	n. 복제 생물, 클론; 복제하다
327	v. 기절시키다, 망연자실하게 만들다	367	v. 조롱하다, 경멸하다; n. 조롱, 경멸	407	v. (씨를) 뿌리다	447	v. 마음에 품다, 고안하다, 상상하다; 이해하다
328	v. 악보로 표시하다; 기록하다, 적어두다	368	v. ~을 능가하다, ~보다 낫다	408	v. (가구를) 비치하다, 제공하다	448	p. 한마디로
329	n. 냄새, 악취	369	a. 먹기에 좋은	409	v. 가리키다, 나타내다; 임명하다	449	p. ~할 수 밖에 없다
330	n. 저당물, 담보, 보증	370	v. 압축하다, 꽉 누르다	410	a. 유능한, 숙련된	450	a. 수직의, 세로의
331	a. 잔인한, 사악한	371	n. ~의 본보기가 되다	411	v. 적합하다 n. 정장; 소송	451	a. 끝의, 밖의, 영구적인
332	p. A를 끌어내다	372	v. 보내다, 전송하다; 전도하다; 전염시키다	412	v. 고갈시키다, 소모시키다	452	p. ~에 따라 행동하다, 조치를 취하다
333	v. 보존하다, 보호하다	373	v. 닦다, 윤내다 n. 광택제	413	v. 허락하다, 인가하다	453	v. (어깨를) 으쓱하다
334	v. 찌르다; 자극하다 n. 아픔, 날카로움	374	n. 눈의, 시각의; 빛을 이용하는	414	v. 따라잡다, 앞지르다	454	v. 번창하다, 잘 자라다
335	v. 조정하다, 중재하다	375	n. 백과사전	415	n. 감사	455	v. 흡수하다, 받아들이다
336	n. (시계의) 추, 진자	376	a. 대가가 큰, 비용이 많이 드는	416	p. ~가 한창일 때	456	a. 돌연한, 갑작스러운
337	n. 운명, 파멸, 죽음	377	n. 운명, 숙명	417	n. 마구간; 매점; 가판대; 칸막이 벽, 칸	457	v. ~탓으로 돌리다; n. 속성, 성질
338	v. 생각해내다, 회상하다	378	v. 경감시키다, 완화시키다	418	v. (명령, 요구 등에) 따르다, 준수하다	458	v. 거두절미한, 간결한
339	n. 제비; v. 삼키다	379	a. 얇은, 순수한	419	v. (주장 등을) 뒷받침하다; 토대를 제공하다	459	n. 공문서; 외교
340	v. 부착하다, 고수하다, 지지하다	380	p. ~에서 자신의 몫을 다하다	420	v. 부유하게 하다, 풍요롭게 하다	460	n. 돌연변이, 변화, 변천

번호	정답 (page 29)	번호	정답 (page 32)	번호	정답 (page 35)	번호	정답 (page 38)
341	verdict	381	adolescent	421	resist	461	aptitude
342	rejoice	382	release	422	spontaneous	462	embassy
343	answer for	383	reverse	423	burglar	463	imprint
344	ethics	384	grant	424	monetary	464	displease
345	fall away	385	inspect	425	break the news to	465	unanimous
346	carefree	386	sacred	426	disorder	466	outspoken
347	depending on	387	obsolete	427	shred	467	catch hold of
348	invest A with B	388	ahead of	428	vague	468	perspective
349	dose	389	enlightenment	429	phenomenon	469	frantic
350	blame A on B	390	administration	430	accuse	470	fertile
351	encounter	391	a bunch of	431	empathic	471	insofar as
352	reprove	392	gulf	432	devote	472	ritual
353	tyrant	393	defect	433	reduce	473	lure
354	on one hand	394	mandatory	434	primitive	474	revalidate
355	dynamic	395	publicity	435	decree	475	detach
356	renown	396	inspire	436	be aimed at	476	speculate
357	throne	397	demote	437	cradle	477	legislate
358	duplicate	398	in case of	438	beloved	478	ban
359	linger	399	liken	439	deadly	479	regress
360	fall into place	400	end up	440	symmetry	480	terrific

Day 13 / Day 14 / Day 15 / Day 16

번호	정답 (page 40)	번호	정답 (page 43)	번호	정답 (page 46)	번호	정답 (page 49)
481	p. A다 B라기 보다는	521	p. 계약을 맺다	561	n. 팽창 v. 부풀다, 부풀어 오르다	601	n. 불면증
482	v. 나아가게 하다, 추진하다	522	v. 평행하다, 유사하다	562	p. 조금은, 어느 정도	602	n. 소외감
483	v. 해고하다, 무시하다; 일축하다, 해산시키다	523	p. (계획, 제의 등을) 받아들이다 / 어울리다	563	a. 강박적인, 충동적인	603	p. ~을 닮다
484	v. 흡입하다	524	n. 사기, 사기꾼	564	p. 전혀 ~이 아닌, ~와는 거리가 먼	604	a. 타고난, 선천적인
485	n. 테, 쇠테, 링, 굴렁쇠	525	v. 이용하다; 개발하다; n. 공, 업적	565	n. 시도, 노력, v. 시도하다	605	p. 평화롭게; 안심하고; 의좋게; 죽어서
486	n. 논평, 해설	526	n. 보도, 방송, 보급	566	v. 미끄러지듯 가다, 활공하다	606	n. 탐욕, 식탐
487	v. 추적하다; 밝혀내다; n. 자취, 발자국	527	v. 빼다, 감하다	567	a. 상관하지 않는, 고려하지 않고	607	v. 임명하다, 공천하다
488	v. 질문하다; n. 질문, 의문	528	n. 가르침, 원리, 주의, 학설	568	v. 확신시키다, 보장하다	608	v. 주지 않다, 받지 않다, 억제하다
489	v. 소홀히 하다, 경시하다; n. 태만, 경시	529	n. 부분, 조각 v. 분할하다	569	n. 비축, 비축량 v. 비축하다	609	v. 제거하다, 없애다
490	v. 추론하다; 암시하다	530	v. 할당하다, 배당하다	570	n. 도구; v. 실행하다, 시행하다	610	v. ~보다 뛰어나다
491	v. 가까이 쓰다; ~탓으로 돌리다	531	a. 이름 없는 n. 익명	571	a. 결심이 굳은, 단호한	611	a. 기이한, 기묘한
492	n. 장관, 성직자, 목사	532	v. 과장하다	572	v. A에게 B를 수여하다	612	v. 평하다, 생각하다 n. 평판, 소문
493	p. ~로부터 떨어져	533	v. 동의하다, 승인하다 n. 동의, 허가	573	n. 가설	613	p. (소식·정보를) 알아내다
494	v. 정렬시키다; 잘 차려 입히다 n. 대형, 배치	534	v. 기껏해야	574	v. (행동, 생각을) 같이하다, 순응하다	614	a. 원인이 되는
495	n. 재앙	535	n. 유입, 유입량	575	n. 국회 v. 모이다	615	p. ~을 받다, ~을 겪다
496	a. 비열한, 비천한	536	a. 모호한, 여러 가지로 해석할 수 있는	576	a. 공손한, 정중한	616	n. 미신, 미신적 행위
497	p. ~일리가 있다, 장점이 있다	537	a. 사나운, 맹렬한	577	p. ~을 두려워[경외]하다	617	p. 위에서, 위로부터
498	v. (불을 붙이다), 태우다	538	v. 차지하다, 점령하다	578	v. 비롯되다, 유래하다; 끌어내다, 유도하다	618	v. 암살하다
499	n. 합성물, 합성어 v. 혼합하다, 합성하다	539	v. 파묻다, 매장하다	579	n. 목수	619	v. (껍질을) 벗기다; 옷을 벗다; 이탈하다
500	a. 불의, 불같은, 화염의	540	p. ~에게 생각이 떠오르다	580	p. ~에 기초하다	620	a. 성숙한, 신중한

번호	정답 (page 41)	번호	정답 (page 44)	번호	정답 (page 47)	번호	정답 (page 50)
501	immense	541	bribe	581	allow for	621	complement
502	stride	542	obedient	582	equipped with	622	silhouette
503	untapped	543	out of date	583	suppress	623	nourish
504	thrift	544	violence	584	prohibit	624	tense
505	obvious	545	gasp	585	struggle	625	in decline
506	autonomy	546	in harmony with	586	commemorate	626	at the beginning of
507	wield	547	at the heart of	587	fixate	627	obesity
508	cut from the same cloth	548	primary	588	fascinate	628	in one's interest
509	excuse oneself for	549	withdraw	589	initiate	629	mast
510	yearn	550	overwhelm	590	with A in mind	630	pedestrian
511	sew	551	at all costs	591	complicate	631	connect with
512	on the contrary	552	radius	592	multitude	632	dispose of
513	coincide with	553	eligible	593	stubborn	633	grasp
514	manipulate	554	get a handle on	594	undertake	634	drown
515	cast A aside	555	census	595	halve	635	tragic
516	come to one's rescue	556	moderate	596	embrace	636	famine
517	prompt	557	orbit	597	defiance	637	lad
518	fulfill	558	be scared of	598	to that end	638	approve of
519	be exposed to	559	accumulate	599	substance	639	sway
520	enchant	560	vanish	600	factual	640	have something to do with

Day 17

번호	정답
641	p. B보다 A를 더 선호하다
642	p. 가까이에
643	n. 해군대장, 제독
644	p. ~의 방법으로, ~에 의해서, ~을 거쳐서
645	a. 세계적인, 국제적인
646	a. 선형의, 선적인
647	p. ~의 영향을 받지 않는
648	a. 적시의, 시기 적절한
649	v. 얻다, 획득하다
650	p. ~에 사로잡힌
651	p. 의무적으로 ~해야 하다
652	n. 포로 a. 사로잡힌, 억류된
653	n. 땀, 발한; 엄청난 노력
654	n. 소매, 소매상 a. 소매의, 소매상의
655	n. 박차, 자극 v. 원동력이 되다
656	n. 공산주의
657	p. ~와 연락하여, ~와 접촉하여
658	p. ~와 공통으로 / ~과 같게
659	n. 입장, 태도, 자세
660	p. 도와주다

page 53

번호	정답
661	catch oneself
662	manufacture
663	in favor with
664	eject
665	profit
666	enormous
667	be prone to do
668	prestige
669	endanger
670	illiterate
671	enroll
672	crack
673	malnutrition
674	cluster
675	folklore
676	cavity
677	compassion
678	admit
679	take hold
680	combustion

Day 18

page 55

번호	정답
681	v. 의뢰하다; 주문하다 n. 위원회; 후견인
682	v. 묻다, 조사하다
683	v. (돈, 시간, 노력 등을) 쏟다, 들이다
684	n. 문지기, 수위, 관리인
685	a. 통렬한, 튼튼한; n. 흑맥주
686	n. 외양간, 헛간
687	v. 처형하다; 실행하다
688	adv. 이에 의하여, 이로써
689	v. 칭찬하다; 맡기다, 위탁하다
690	v. 구별하다, 구분하다
691	p. 늦어도 ~까지는
692	a. 하위의; 부차적인, 부수적인; n. 부하
693	p. 시기 적절하게
694	p. 도움을 요청하다; 입대하다
695	p. 발달한 상태가 되다, 성년이 되다
696	n. 행동, 행위, 사실, 실행; 권리증서
697	v. 잘라버리다; 서둘러 떠나다
698	p. 많은, 다량의
699	v. 마비시키다, 활동 불능이 되게 하다
700	n. 가시; 고통을 주는 것

page 56

번호	정답
701	obsess
702	warrant
703	starve
704	be divided into
705	exclusive
706	scheme
707	condense
708	composure
709	consonant
710	anticipate
711	alchemy
712	urge
713	cemetery
714	adjust to N
715	physiology
716	crawl
717	under consideration
718	delegate
719	verify
720	tolerate

Day 19

page 58

번호	정답
721	v. 일치하다, 조화되다 n. 합의
722	p. 외견상으로는
723	p. 차례로
724	v. 억압하다
725	v. 알아보다, 식별하다; 인정하다
726	p. ~하는 것으로 보이다
727	n. 속기, 약칭 v. 속기하다
728	p. 할인하여
729	n. 부동산
730	a. 엄격한, 가차없는, 혹독한
731	n. 이익, 목적, 위험
732	p. ~와 제휴하여, 협력하여
733	v. 압축하다, 죄다
734	p. 다루다, 대처하다
735	n. 적자, 부족액, 결손
736	v. ~와 일치하다
737	v. 해임하다, 내보내다, 방출하다; 이행하다
738	n. 계약금, 예약금, 예금; 퇴적물, 침전물
739	n. 부족, 결핍
740	v. 세게 밀다; 찌르다

page 59

번호	정답
741	neutral
742	worship
743	attain
744	meditate
745	misuse
746	divine
747	consecutive
748	fad
749	murmur
750	at an early age
751	component
752	flavor
753	impolite
754	take pride in
755	paradox
756	intense
757	downplay
758	smother
759	fraction
760	come across

Day 20

page 61

번호	정답
761	n. 지루함
762	v. 드러내다, 나타내다, 보여주다
763	v. 확신시키다, 납득시키다, 수긍하게 하다
764	v. 내던지다, 퍼붓다
765	n. 위생
766	n. 모피, 털
767	a. 강한; 심오한; 깊은 n. 깊은 바다(심연)
768	n. 필수품 a. 필요한
769	p. ~에게 부과되다, ~ 맡겨지다; ~을 습격하다
770	n. 등장, 출현
771	v. 한정하다, 제한하다; 가두다, 감금하다
772	v. 항의(하다)
773	n. 하수, 오물, 오수
774	a. 익은, 숙성한
775	n. 통계; 통계학, 통계 자료
776	p. 자기 방식이 몸에 밴
777	p. 차례로, 잇따라서, 하나하나
778	a. 빽빽한, 밀집한, 짙은
779	n. 교육; 수업료
780	p. 그만큼 더

page 62

번호	정답
781	county
782	conduct
783	superb
784	be familiar with
785	mimic
786	dedicate
787	couple A with B
788	distribute
789	genuine
790	straightforward
791	cite
792	clean out
793	exclaim
794	by now
795	mischance
796	outset
797	faint
798	adequate
799	in the same way
800	hit the books

Day 21

page 64

번호	정답
801	v. 영향을 주다, 작용하다; ~인 체하다
802	p. ~에 대한
803	n. 장비, 병기
804	v. 강화하다, 요새화하다
805	a. 정교주의, 매우 아름다운
806	n. 활동; 업무, 사건, 스캔들; 불륜, 정사
807	v. 번영하다, 성공하다
808	p. 게다가, 더욱이
809	n. 선구자, 선도자
810	a. 많은
811	n. 비율; 조화, 균형
812	p. 어떠한 경우에도
813	v. 공들여 만들다 n. 공예, 기술
814	p. (알람·경보 등이) 울리다
815	v. 탐닉하다, ~에 빠지다; 내버려 두다
816	v. 선언하다, 공표하다
817	a. 널리 퍼져 있는 n. 유행(병)
818	p. ~에서 회복하다
819	p. ~을 좋아하다
820	p. ~에 대한 헌신

page 65

번호	정답
821	consistent with
822	discourse
823	homicide
824	in the absence of
825	moral
826	have a problem with
827	monastery
828	decade
829	wither
830	soothe
831	attract A to B
832	calculate
833	incorporate
834	correlated with
835	come up with
836	render
837	vegetation
838	barometer
839	get A out
840	depress

Day 22

page 67

번호	정답
841	p. 운동하다; 알아내다, 해결하다; 계산하다
842	v. 구두점을 찍다, (말을) 중단시키다
843	n. 기부, 기여, 공헌; 원인제공
844	v. 멈추다; 급히 떠나다
845	n. 상인, 무역상
846	p. 돌아다니다
847	n. 신용 v. 신용하다
848	p. ~을 이용[활용]하다
849	v. 주장하다, 공언하다; ~인 체하다
850	n. 적, 원수
851	n. 충동, 자극
852	v. 말로 가리키다, 나타내다, 암시하다
853	v. 오르다; 승진하다
854	n. 치우친 사랑, 편애
855	p. ~을 물려주다
856	n. 적개심
857	n. (지구를) 동일하게 나누는 것, 적도
858	v. 더럽히다, 오염시키다
859	v. 억제하다
860	n. 애도; v. 애통하다

page 68

번호	정답
861	ballot
862	resign
863	impersonal
864	impose A on B
865	reap
866	colony
867	gracious
868	bring about
869	at one another
870	unease
871	ware
872	perceive
873	come about
874	align
875	detective
876	submerge
877	refer to N
878	tumble
879	valid
880	inherent

Day 23

page 70

번호	정답
881	n. 군중, 폭도, 떼
882	a. 지급 능력이 있는; 용해력이 있는; 용매, 용제
883	p. ~하기 위한
884	v. 키를 잡다, 조종하다; 이끌다, 나아가게 하다
885	v. 방해하다, 어지럽히다
886	a. 익은; 음력의
887	v. 관련시키다; 교제하다 n. 동료, 친구
888	v. 묘사하다, 서술하다
889	v. 숨기다
890	v. 방해하다, 간섭하다
891	v. 확산시키다, 분산되다
892	p. A를 B와 혼동하다
893	p. ~를 줄이다
894	n. 겁쟁이
895	p. 바로 지금, 이 순간에도
896	v. 동면하다
897	v. 기르다, 양육하다
898	p. 지금
899	p. ~가 편한 때에
900	n. 섭씨

page 71

번호	정답
901	omit
902	inflame
903	coffin
904	chop up
905	utter
906	confidential
907	reinforce
908	shatter
909	engage
910	inherit from
911	sufficient
912	a quantity of
913	interface
914	exotic
915	district
916	adapt to N
917	torture
918	in the air
919	do away with
920	indifferent

Day 24

page 73

번호	정답
921	p. ~을 얻으려고 노력하다
922	p. 침입하다
923	p. 직접 만날 수 있는
924	v. 시작하다, 시작되다, 개시하다; 학위를 받다
925	v. 가정하다, 추측하다; 떠맡다; ~인 체하다
926	a. 고급의, 사양이 높은
927	n. 떼, 무리; 떼 지어가다
928	v. 변환하다, 전환하다, 개종시키다
929	v. 끈으로 묶다, 꾸러미싸다, 한묶음싸다, 다발싸다
930	p. 고집하다
931	a. 지나간, 과거의
932	n. 저주; v. 저주하다
933	a. 우울한
934	v. 노력하다, 노력하다, 애쓰다
935	n. 주석(원소기호 Sn), 통조림; (원통형) 통
936	v. 딴 데로 돌리다, 산만하게 하다
937	a. 신진대사의, 물질대사의
938	p. 설명하다; (부분·비율을) 차지하다
939	v. 막다, 방해하다
940	n. 유산, 유물, 물려받은 것

page 74

번호	정답
941	sequence
942	perish
943	resolve
944	linguistic
945	extinct
946	reckless
947	cling
948	pregnant
949	manifest
950	aspiration
951	mourn
952	entrust
953	strife
954	dispatch
955	extract
956	come to do
957	exhaust
958	at times
959	go along with
960	hazard

Day 25

page 76

번호	정답
961	n. 노래가사; a. 서정시의
962	p. ~을 상대하다, 다루다
963	v. 붕괴시키다, 분열시키다, 방해하다
964	v. 지키다, 준수하다; 관찰하다
965	v. 울타리로 가로 막다, 난처하다
966	n. 인용구, 인용; 견적
967	a. 위태로운, 위험한, 비판적인; 중요한
968	v. 실을 꿰다 n. 실
969	a. 연속적인, 연이은
970	n. 분리; 인종 차별
971	p. ~ 비난을 받아야 한다, ~의 책임이 있다
972	v. 요구하다, 청구하다; 수요
973	v. 금지하다, 방해하다
974	a. 무자비한, 냉정한
975	v. 더욱 (목적이) 동일하다, 모으다 n. 조립
976	p. 결론적으로, 끝으로
977	n. 하부조직(구조), 기초, 토대; 사회 기반 시설
978	n. 높이, 고도, 해발
979	a. 몹시 추운, 냉담한
980	v. 증언하다, 진술하다

page 77

번호	정답
981	blow away
982	contemplate
983	in good faith
984	mindlessly
985	in passing
986	at all times
987	parachute
988	strain
989	resemble
990	be accustomed to N
991	inevitable
992	summit
993	impartial
994	temperate
995	dominate
996	after the fact
997	hand over
998	commodity
999	optimal
1000	assert

이그잼보카 고등 1000 4월

발 행 | 2024년 3월 6일
저 자 | 김동원
펴낸이 | 한건희
펴낸곳 | 주식회사 부크크
출판사등록 | 2014.07.15(제2014-16호)
주 소 | 서울특별시 금천구 가산디지털1로 110 SK트윈타워 A동 305호
전 화 | 1670-8316
이메일 | info@bookk.co.kr

ISBN | 979-11-410-7522-4

www.bookk.co.kr
ⓒ 김동원 2024
